SPELLING YEAR 2

Ages 6–7

M SCHOLASTIC

Published in the UK by Scholastic Education, 2020
Book End, Range Road, Witney,
Oxfordshire, OX29 0YD
A division of Scholastic Limited

London – New York – Toronto – Sydney – Auckland
Mexico City – New Delhi – Hong Kong

www.scholastic.co.uk

1 2 3 4 5 6 7 8 9 0 1 2 3 4 5 6 7 8 9

British Library Cataloguing-in-Publication Data
A catalogue record for this book is available from the British Library.

ISBN 978-1407-18346-6

Printed and bound in Great Britain by Bell and Bain Ltd, Glasgow

Papers used by Scholastic Limited are made from wood grown in sustainable forests.

Author
Shelley Welsh

Editorial
Rachel Morgan, Vicki Yates, Suzanne Adams, Julia Roberts

Design
Dipa Mistry and QBS Learning

Cover Illustration
Clau Souza @Bright Agency

Illustration
Clau Souza

Spelling test transcripts

Spelling Test 1

Spelling 1: The word is **tumble**.
Gerraint began to **tumble** down the hill.
The word is **tumble**.

Spelling 2: The word is **happiness**.
Our new dog has brought a lot of **happiness**.
The word is **happiness**.

Spelling 3: The word is **running**.
We like **running** across the playground.
The word is **running**.

Spelling 4: The word is **flies**.
The teacher wafted the **flies** out of the window.
The word is **flies**.

Spelling 5: The word is **cinema**.
Grandpa is taking me to the **cinema** tonight.
The word is **cinema**.

Spelling 6: The word is **wrote**.
We **wrote** thank-you notes to our grandparents.
The word is **wrote**.

Spelling 7: The word is **orange**.
Dad peeled an **orange** for me.
The word is **orange**.

Spelling 8: The word is **gardener**.
My mum is a keen **gardener**.
The word is **gardener**.

Spelling 9: The word is **juicy**.
Ben ate a **juicy** apple at lunchtime.
The word is **juicy**.

Spelling 10: The word is **giraffes**.
I liked the **giraffes** best at the zoo.
The word is **giraffes**.

Spelling Test 2

Spelling 1: The word is **wrap**.
We **wrap** up in warm clothes when it's cold.
The word is **wrap**.

Spelling 2: The word is **join**.
I used glue to **join** the paper.
The word is **join**.

Spelling 3: The word is **married**.
My grandparents have been **married** for forty years.
The word is **married**.

Spelling 4: The word is **shopping**.
Mum and I went **shopping** for new shoes.
The word is **shopping**.

Spelling 5: The word is **icy**.
We take care to walk slowly when it's **icy**.
The word is **icy**.

Spelling 6: The word is **silliness**.
Our teacher told us to stop our **silliness**.
The word is **silliness**.

Spelling 7: The word is **slimy**.
There was a **slimy** mess in the art area.
The word is **slimy**.

Spelling 8: The word is **mention**.
Mum didn't **mention** her broken vase.
The word is **mention**.

Spelling 9: The word is **squirrel**.
The **squirrel** gathered nuts for its nest.
The word is **squirrel**.

Spelling 10: The word is **pleasure**.
It was a **pleasure** to watch the choir sing.
The word is **pleasure**.

Spelling test transcripts

Spelling Test 3

Spelling 1: The word is **laziest**.
Our dog is the **laziest** dog in the world.
The word is **laziest**.

Spelling 2: The word is **evil**.
The **evil** creature lived in a cave.
The word is **evil**.

Spelling 3: The word is **condition**.
Mum's car is old but in good **condition**.
The word is **condition**.

Spelling 4: The word is **lovely**.
We had a **lovely** meal in the restaurant.
The word is **lovely**.

Spelling 5: The word is **equipment**.
I helped set out the PE **equipment**.
The word is **equipment**.

Spelling 6: The word is **hummed**.
Gran **hummed** a catchy tune.
The word is **hummed**.

Spelling 7: The word is **herd**.
A **herd** of cows wandered across the lane.
The word is **herd**.

Spelling 8: The word is **nation**.
The whole **nation** screamed when they won the cup.
The word is **nation**.

Spelling 9: The word is **wrestled**.
The policeman **wrestled** the robber to the ground.
The word is **wrestled**.

Spelling 10: The word is **vision**.
The optician will check my **vision**.
The word is **vision**.

Spelling Test 4

Spelling 1: The word is **shovel**.
Mum used a **shovel** to dig the garden.
The word is **shovel**.

Spelling 2: The word is **hoping**.
I am **hoping** for a new bike for my birthday.
The word is **hoping**.

Spelling 3: The word is **trace**.
The stranger disappeared without a **trace**.
The word is **trace**.

Spelling 4: The word is **headache**.
When it's too hot I get a **headache**.
The word is **headache**.

Spelling 5: The word is **their**.
The children tidied **their** room.
The word is **their**.

Spelling 6: The word is **stunned**.
We were **stunned** that our teacher was leaving.
The word is **stunned**.

Spelling 7: The word is **lifeless**.
In winter, our garden seems quite **lifeless**.
The word is **lifeless**.

Spelling 8: The word is **knit**.
Dad helped me **knit** a scarf for my teddy.
The word is **knit**.

Spelling 9: The word is **subtraction**.
I am improving at **subtraction**.
The word is **subtraction**.

Spelling 10: The word is **quality**.
My school uniform is good **quality**.
The word is **quality**.

Spelling test transcripts

Spelling Test 5

Spelling 1: The word is **tremble**.
Beth began to **tremble** with the cold.
The word is **tremble**.

Spelling 2: The word is **boxed**.
The thug **boxed** the policeman and ran off.
The word is **boxed**.

Spelling 3: The word is **hopping**.
Dan likes **hopping** on one leg.
The word is **hopping**.

Spelling 4: The word is **city**.
Mum and Dad are going on a **city** break.
The word is **city**.

Spelling 5: The word is **knot**.
There is a **knot** in my shoelace.
The word is **knot**.

Spelling 6: The word is **replacement**.
Today, we have a **replacement** teacher.
The word is **replacement**.

Spelling 7: The word is **sighed**.
Jamal **sighed** when he started the test.
The word is **sighed**.

Spelling 8: The word is **journeys**.
I love going on long train **journeys**.
The word is **journeys**.

Spelling 9: The word is **indication**.
There had been no **indication** that it would rain so hard.
The word is **indication**.

Spelling 10: The word is **measure**.
The teacher showed us how to **measure** the ingredients.
The word is **measure**.

Spelling Test 6

Spelling 1: The word is **copied**.
Bhavini **copied** down her spellings.
The word is **copied**.

Spelling 2: The word is **charge**.
The cows **charge** across the field at feeding time.
The word is **charge**.

Spelling 3: The word is **cute**.
Bella's new kitten is very **cute**.
The word is **cute**.

Spelling 4: The word is **gnome**.
Our neighbours have a **gnome** in their garden.
The word is **gnome**.

Spelling 5: The word is **fixed**.
Mum **fixed** my bike.
The word is **fixed**.

Spelling 6: The word is **animals**.
Elephants are my favourite **animals**.
The word is **animals**.

Spelling 7: The word is **fancy**.
Tia wore a **fancy** hat for the parade.
The word is **fancy**.

Spelling 8: The word is **giant**.
Ollie saw a **giant** spider in the garden.
The word is **giant**.

Spelling 9: The word is **payment**.
The **payment** for the school trip is due today.
The word is **payment**.

Spelling 10: The word is **squash**.
I love orange and blackcurrant **squash**.
The word is **squash**.

Spelling Test 7

Spelling 1: The word is **frying**.
We began **frying** the mushrooms.
The word is **frying**.

Spelling 2: The word is **wrong**.
I was hoping it wasn't the **wrong** answer.
The word is **wrong**.

Spelling 3: The word is **drumming**.
Ahmed was **drumming** on the table.
The word is **drumming**.

Spelling 4: The word is **huge**.
Last night, there was a **huge** storm.
The word is **huge**.

Spelling 5: The word is **mixed**.
We **mixed** the flour with the eggs.
The word is **mixed**.

Spelling 6: The word is **knock**.
There was a loud **knock** on the door.
The word is **knock**.

Spelling 7: The word is **playful**.
My puppy is very **playful**.
The word is **playful**.

Spelling 8: The word is **spicy**.
Freda loves **spicy** food.
The word is **spicy**.

Spelling 9: The word is **noisiest**.
Martha is the **noisiest** girl in our class.
The word is **noisiest**.

Spelling 10: The word is **decision**.
I made the **decision** to read to the end of the book.
The word is **decision**.

Progress chart

Fill in your score in the table below to see how well you've done.

Test number	Score	Percentage
Spelling Test 1	/10	
Spelling Test 2	/10	
Spelling Test 3	/10	
Spelling Test 4	/10	
Spelling Test 5	/10	
Spelling Test 6	/10	
Spelling Test 7	/10	

Percentage	
0–33%	Good try! You need more practice in some topics – ask an adult to help you.
34–69%	You're doing really well. Ask for extra help for any topics you found tricky.
70–100%	You're a 10-Minute SATs Test star – good work!

Reward Certificate

Well done!

You have completed all of the 10-Minute SATs Tests

Name: _____   Date: _____

SATs Made Simple

English

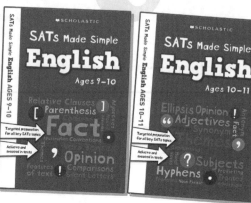

Maths

➡ **Covers all English and Maths SATs test topics**

➡ **Includes fun activities and skills check questions**

➡ **Ideal for extra practice at home**

Contents

How to use this book

This book contains twelve different spelling practices based on key spelling topics to be covered in Year 2. There are also seven mixed spelling tests.

Spelling practice

Throughout each spelling practice there are short explanations recapping the rules or the focus and providing further guidance where necessary. There are up to five questions in each spelling practice, which challenge the children to complete parts of words or sentences, sort spellings into categories, complete crosswords or word searches, and so on.

At the end of each practice section, you will find a weekly spelling list and a section for children to note down any spellings they struggled with. Ask your child to practise the weekly spelling lists using Look-Cover-Write-Check, employing the skills they have learned. Encourage them to write down words they need more practice with in the 'words I struggled with' space and encourage them to practise these words too. It is intended that children will take around ten minutes to complete each spelling practice.

Spelling tests

There are ten questions in each spelling test which amount to ten marks. Read each spelling number followed by *The word is...* Leave at least a 12-second gap between spellings. More information can be found on page 58.

Spelling the /j/ sound
Spelling Practice 1

10 MINS

When the /j/ sound follows a short vowel sound, it is spelled **dge**: **badge**.

When the /j/ sound follows a long vowel sound or a consonant, it is spelled **ge**: **huge**, **charge**.

I. Add either **dge** or **ge** to each group of letters below to make a word. Say the word out loud to hear the vowel sound before you write it.

pa_____   ri_____   sta_____

fu_____   bri_____   le_____

ra_____   nu_____   fri_____

smu_____   oran_____   hin_____

CHECK IN A DICTIONARY

2. Solve the clues and fill in the missing letters to make the /j/ sound.

You can slide down a snowy slope in this

s	l	e			

Mum might cut this when it grows too tall.

h	e			

Our hamster lives in one of these.

c			

The opposite of small.

l	a			

A black and white animal.

b	a				

Spelling the /j/ sound
Spelling Practice 1

The /j/ sound spelled **j** is usually seen at the beginning of words. It is often followed by **a**, **o** or **u**: **jump**.

The /j/ sound is usually spelled **g** before **e**, **i** and **y**: **giant**.

3. There is one word with a /j/ sound spelled incorrectly in each sentence below. Circle the word, then write the correct spelling on the line.

Dad bought me a new blue gacket.

_____

Ash likes gam on his toast.

_____

At the zoo, we saw monkeys and jiraffes.

_____

Ted used glue to goin the paper.

_____

After PE, I had no enerjy left.

_____

Weekly spelling list:

badge	edge	dodge	fudge
ridge	rage	huge	charge
strange	jam	jacket	join
jar	energy	magic	giant

Words I struggled with:

Well done! END OF SPELLING PRACTICE 1!

START

Words ending le, el, al, il

Spelling Practice 2

10 MINS

Most words that end in an /ul/ sound have the spelling **le**. Some words with this sound are spelled with **el**, **al** or **il**.

You will often find the **el** spelling after the letters **m**, **n**, **r**, **s**, **v** and **w**.

I. Write these words in the correct places in the table below.

tumble   pencil   tunnel   thimble   nostril   travel

towel   petal   pedal   cable   capital   pupil

le ending		el ending	
al ending		**il** ending	

2. The following words have been spelled as they sound, with the wrong ending, **ul**. Decide which ending each should have (**al**, **il**, **le** or **el**), then write the word correctly on the line.

squir**rul** _____

ani**mul** _____

sten**cul** _____

comforta**bul** _____

3. Add the missing ending to each word in the sentences below.

Ciara's dad used a shov_____ to dig the garden.

My grandma is in hospit_____ but she is feeling better.

We studied a foss_____ that was thousands of years old.

Faisal heard the distant rumb_____ of thunder.

KEEP IT GOING!

Weekly spelling list:

LOOK
COVER
WRITE
CHECK ✔

fossil	pencil	nostril	pupil
shovel	pedal	rumble	thimble
tumble	tremble	hospital	capital
squirrel	towel	plural	snivel

Words I struggled with:

Well done! END OF SPELLING PRACTICE 2!

11

Suffixes 1
Spelling Practice 3

If a root word ends in **y** with a consonant before it, the **y** is changed to **i** before adding the suffixes **ed**, **es**, **er** and **est**: **tidy**, **tidied**, **tidies**, **tidier**, **tidiest**.

1. Add **ed** and **es** to each of the following words.

   carry _____ _____

   copy _____ _____

   marry _____ _____

   cry _____ _____

   worry _____ _____

2. Write the correct form of the word in bold on the line.

   Josh is **heavy** but Petra is _____.

   Sol is **funny** but Fabian is _____.

   Mia is **lazy** but Fred is _____.

   Sophie is **nosy** but Luca is _____.

3. Complete the table below.

crazy	crazier	craziest
	lonelier	loneliest
angry		
	happier	
busy		
	noisier	

If you add the suffix **ing** to a word that ends in **y**, you keep the **y: tidying**.

4. Add **ing** to each word in brackets and write it on the line.

Flo's mum is (fry) _____ onions.

I was (carry) _____ the shopping for Dad.

Syd is (try) _____ to tidy his bedroom.

Priti was (copy) _____ her sister.

Weekly spelling list:

copy	copies	copied	copying
marry	marries	married	heavy
heavier	heaviest	tiny	tinier
tiniest	happy	happier	happiest

Words I struggled with:

_____

_____

_____

_____

_____

_____

Well done! END OF SPELLING PRACTICE 3!

Suffixes 2
Spelling Practice 4

10 MINS

If a root word ends in **e** with a consonant before it, the **e** is dropped before adding **ed**, **er**, **est**, **y** and **ing**.

1. Add the suffixes **ed** and **ing** to each of the following words.

   like   _____   _____

   love   _____   _____

   stare   _____   _____

   close   _____   _____

2. Add the suffixes **er** and **est** to the word in bold to complete each sentence.

   My painting is **nice**, Niamh's painting is _____ but Lyle's is the _____.

   Although this puppy is **cute**, that one is _____ and that one over there is the _____.

   Archie arrived **late**, Freddie came even _____ but Ahmed was the _____.

3. Solve the clues and fill in the missing letters.

Someone who makes bread and cakes.

b				

The author of a book.

w					

A person who moves to music.

d					

Someone who looks after plants.

g							

4. Add the suffix **y** to each word and write the new word on the line. Remember the spelling rule!

bone _____   laze _____

noise _____   slime _____

10 MINS

Weekly spelling list:

love	loved	loving	stare
stared	staring	nice	nicer
nicest	cute	cuter	cutest
write	writer	noise	noisy

Words I struggled with:

Well done! END OF SPELLING PRACTICE 4!

Suffixes 3
Spelling Practice 5

10 MINS

If a root word has one syllable and ends in a single consonant after a single vowel, the last consonant is doubled when adding **ed**, **ing**, **er**, **est** or **y**.

1. Add the suffixes **ed** and **ing** to each of the following words.

   hum   _____   _____

   drop   _____   _____

   rip   _____   _____

   clip   _____   _____

   tap   _____   _____

2. Write the correct version of the word in brackets on the line in each sentence.

   We watched the (run) _____ win the race.

   Kamal thought the film was very (fun) _____ .

   I was the (win) _____ of the competition.

   I've just eaten the (big) _____ ice cream!

3. Circle one word that is incorrect in each sentence. Write the correct spellings on the lines underneath.

I chose the fatest puppy in the pet shop.

_____

My coat is much thiner than yours.

_____

What a beautiful, suny day it is!

_____

Polly's dad is a brilliant drumer.

_____

Dan's old jumper is rather sagy.

_____

KEEP IT GOING!

4. Circle the **four** words in the passage below that follow the spelling rule for doubling consonants when adding a suffix. Write each word on a line below.

> Rhianna was helping Mum in the garden. They were chopping down an old tree when Rhianna almost tripped over the roots! Then they planted some seeds, carefully patting the soil down around them. When they had finished, there was a lot of chatter about the good job they had done.

_____   _____

_____   _____

There is an exception to the rule: the letter **x** is not doubled when you add a suffix.

5. Write the missing words in the spaces below.

	ed	ing	er
mix		mixing	mixer
box	boxed		

Weekly spelling list:

drop	dropped	dropping	pat
patted	patting	trip	tripped
tripping	run	runner	running
box	boxed	boxing	boxer

Words I struggled with:

Well done! END OF SPELLING PRACTICE 5!

21

Suffixes 4
Spelling Practice 6

10 MINS

You can add suffixes that start with a consonant to most root words without changing the last letter of the word.

1. Add the suffix **ment** to each word below.

   enjoy   _____

   agree   _____

   pay   _____

   amaze   _____

   punish   _____

If the root word has more than one syllable and ends in **y** with a consonant before it, the **y** is changed to **i** before adding the suffix: **merry – merriment**.

2. Add either **ment** or **ness** to the root words below.
   Remember the rule for words ending in **y**!

   happy   _____   equip   _____

   replace _____   crispy   _____

   dirty   _____   measure _____

3. Add the ending **ful**, **less**, **ness** or **ly** to each word in brackets. Use each suffix once only.

Miles is quite (hope) _____ with his money.

Meg's (play) _____ puppy is called Monty.

I (quick) _____ tidied my bedroom.

In a moment of (silly) _____, Shay kicked the ball over the hedge.

4. Find and circle these **four** words in the wordsearch.

plainly   pavement   careful   lifeless

x	p	a	v	e	m	e	n	t
y	l	w	m	m	x	k	b	b
c	a	r	e	f	u	l	x	z
z	i	z	x	c	v	b	m	w
r	n	x	v	b	w	x	q	y
q	l	i	f	e	l	e	s	s
z	y	c	v	x	z	q	y	z

10 MINS

Weekly spelling list:

agree	agreement	pay	payment
amaze	amazement	punish	punishment
happy	happiness	happily	silly
silliness	care	careless	careful

Words I struggled with:

Well done! END OF SPELLING PRACTICE 6!

10 MINS

Words that start with the letter **k** or the letter **g** followed by the letter **n** are pronounced with the /n/ sound only. This means the **k** or **g** is silent: **knit** is pronounced 'nit'.

1. Circle the **silent letter** in each word below, then say each word out loud.

   gnome   knot   gnash   gnat   know

2. The words on the left have been written as they sound. Draw a line to match each word with its correct spelling on the right.

Incorrect spelling	Correct spelling
nuckle	knock
nee	knuckle
nock	gnaw
naw	gnash
nob	knee
nash	knob

KEEP IT GOING!

Silent letters

10 MINS

Words that start with the letter **w** followed by the letter **r** are pronounced with the /r/ sound only. This means the **w** is silent: **wrap** is pronounced 'rap'.

3. The following words have been written without their silent letters. Rewrite them correctly on the lines.

rite   _____   rong   _____

riggle   _____   restle   _____

4. Underline the **six** words in the passage below that should have a silent **k**, **g** or **w**. Write the correct words on the lines.

> The night rode his limping horse into the forest, followed by his faithful dog, Sabre. He tied the horse to a tree with a rope, notted it tightly, then looked at her sore nee. He rapped a bandage round it. Nowing he had to get help, he rote a note and gave it to his dog. "Quickly, Sabre, take this to the king."

_____   _____

_____   _____

_____   _____

 **10 MINS**

Weekly spelling list:

 LOOK COVER WRITE CHECK ✔

knot	knotted	knee	knit
knitting	know	knowing	knew
gnat	gnome	gnash	gnaw
wrap	wrapper	wrestle	wrestled

Words I struggled with:

Well done! END OF SPELLING PRACTICE 7!

27

Sometimes, the sound /s/ is spelled **c** before the letters **e**, **i** and **y**.

I. Write these words in the correct places in the table.

pace	city	icy	fancy
trace	price	cinema	cycle
circus	spicy	circle	dance

c before **e**	**c** before **i**	**c** before **y**

KEEP IT GOING!

2. Fill in the grid with the words below. One letter has been done for you.

racer   lacy   force   mercy

1		2		3
4		c		

3. Solve the clues to fill in the missing letters.

An open area.

| s | p | | | |

A six-sided shape that you roll.

| d | | | |

An adjective to describe an apple.

| j | u | i | | |

You might eat this with curry.

| r | | | |

Weekly spelling list:

city	icy	ice	fancy
force	race	racer	trace
price	cinema	cycle	dance
spicy	circle	juice	juicy

Words I struggled with:

_____

_____

_____

_____

_____

_____

Well done! END OF SPELLING PRACTICE 8!

Words ending in tion

Spelling Practice 9

10 MINS

Many words in English end with the sound /shun/. The most common spelling of this ending is **tion**.

If a word ends in **t** or **te**, drop the **t** or **te** before adding **tion**.

I. Add **tion** to each of these words and write the new word on the line next to it. Make any spelling changes that are needed.

subtract _____

invent _____

celebrate _____

correct _____

create _____

KEEP IT GOING!

2. The words below have been spelled as they sound. Rewrite them on the lines with the correct spellings.

indicashun   _____

condishun   _____

injecshun   _____

ficshun   _____

emoshun   _____

3. Unravel the following words that end in **tion**.

tionna   _____

tionmen   _____

tionsta   _____

tioncommunica   _____

tionposi   _____

10 MINS

Weekly spelling list:

subtraction	invention	celebration	invitation
creation	indication	condition	injection
fiction	emotion	nation	mention
station	position	communication	motion

Words I struggled with:

Well done! END OF SPELLING PRACTICE 9!

Compound words
Spelling Practice 10

10 MINS

A compound word is made by joining two words to make one new word.

1. Add a word to each word below to make a new word.

bath + _____ = _____

web + _____ = _____

play + _____ = _____

grand + _____ = _____

shoe + _____ = _____

2. The wrong words have been joined to make the following compound words. Write the correct word on the line next to each.

scare**paper** _____

rain**ball** _____

foot**crow** _____

wall**bow** _____

3. Add another word to the beginning of each of the following to make a compound word. Write each new word on the line. For some words, there is more than one answer.

+ ache _____

+ stairs _____

+ nail _____

+ yard _____

+ drop _____

4. Solve the clues to fill in the missing letters in the words below.

Plants need water and this to grow.

s							

A yellow wild flower.

b								

5. Solve the clues to find two words which join to make compound words. Write the compound word on the line.

Faye ties hers in a ponytail + you use this to paint.

_____ + _____ = _____

A type of shiny yellow metal + a creature that lives in water.

_____ + _____ = _____

Wet weather + something to wear when it's cold.

_____ + _____ = _____

10 MINS

Weekly spelling list:

classroom	website	newspaper	playground
bedtime	upstairs	goldfish	hairbrush
downstairs	dragonfly	farmyard	rainfall
raindrop	rainbow	sunshine	buttercup

Words I struggled with:

Well done! END OF SPELLING PRACTICE 10!

Homophones
Spelling Practice 11

10 MINS

Homophones are words that sound the same but have a different meaning and spelling. Some words sound almost the same and they are called **near-homophones**.

1. Match each word on the left with its homophone on the right.

Homophone

saw

bore

Word

bare

here

pair   two

bear   hear

too   pour

see   pear

sea

toe

10 MINS

2. Complete each sentence with the correct **homophone** from the wordbank below.

red	read	side	sighed
herd	heard	road	rowed

Milo _____ the doorbell.

The farmer counted his _____ of cows.

We drove down the _____ to the farm.

The team _____ the boat over the finish line.

I have _____ my new book already.

Ushma's new gloves are _____ and blue.

Martha _____ as she did her homework.

Kai has a bruise on the _____ of his leg.

KEEP IT GOING!

3. In the sentences below, the wrong homophone has been used. Circle it and write the correct word on the line.

I new I had done well in my test.

_____

Sum children were talking in assembly.

_____

Douglas can right his name backwards.

_____

Mum picked a nice flour for Dad.

_____

Our friends walk there dog every day.

_____

Grandpa took me two school.

_____

This curry is to spicy for me.

_____

10 MINS

Weekly spelling list:

here	hear	bare	bear
pour	pore	red	read
herd	heard	pair	pear
right	write	there	their

Words I struggled with:

_____

_____

_____

_____

_____

Well done! END OF SPELLING PRACTICE 11!

Tricky words

Spelling Practice 12

10 MINS

Many words are not spelled as you would think.

To make the plural of most words ending in **ey**, simply add the suffix **s**.

1. Write the plural of each word below.

key _____

donkey _____

journey _____

2. Now think of other words ending in **ey** where the plural is made in the same way. Write the plural forms on the lines below.

_____

_____

After the letters **w** and **qu**, the most usual spelling for the sound /o/, as in **hot**, is the letter **a**.

3. Fill in the missing letter for the /o/ sound in each word, then use Look-Cover-Write-Check using the additional lines.

squ__sh   _____   _____

qu__lity   _____   _____

w__sp   _____   _____

w__tch   _____   _____

w__nd   _____   _____

KEEP IT GOING!

Some words with a /zh/ sound have the spelling **s**: televi**s**ion.

4. Say the words in the box out loud. Circle the **eight** words that have a /zh/ sound spelled **s**, then write them on the lines below.

vision	judges	division	treasure
sure	pleasure	usual	reason
measure	possession	decision	leisure

_____   _____

_____   _____

_____   _____

_____   _____

10 MINS

Weekly spelling list:

LOOK COVER WRITE CHECK ✔

keys	donkeys	monkeys	valleys
squash	quality	wander	watch
vision	television	division	treasure
pleasure	leisure	decision	usual

Words I struggled with:

Well done! END OF SPELLING PRACTICE 12!

Marks

1. Gerraint began to _____ down the hill.

2. Our new dog has brought a lot of _____.

3. We like _____ across the playground.

4. The teacher wafted the _____ out of the window.

5. Grandpa is taking me to the _____ tonight.

6. We _____ thank-you notes to our grandparents.

7. Dad peeled an _____ for me.

8. My mum is a keen _____.

9. Ben ate a _____ apple at lunchtime.

10. I liked the _____ best at the zoo.

10

Well done! END OF SPELLING TEST 1!

Marks

1. We _____ up in warm clothes when it's cold.

2. I used glue to _____ the paper.

3. My grandparents have been _____ for forty years.

4. Mum and I went _____ for new shoes.

5. We take care to walk slowly when it's _____.

6. Our teacher told us to stop our _____.

7. There was a _____ mess in the art area.

8. Mum didn't _____ her broken vase.

9. The _____ gathered nuts for its nest.

10. It was a _____ to watch the choir sing.

10

Well done! END OF SPELLING TEST 2!

Marks

1. Our dog is the _____ dog in the world.

2. The _____ creature lived in a cave.

3. Mum's car is old but in good _____.

4. We had a _____ meal in the restaurant.

5. I helped set out the PE _____.

6. Gran _____ a catchy tune.

7. A _____ of cows wandered across the lane.

8. The whole _____ screamed when they won the cup.

9. The policeman _____ the robber to the ground.

10. The optician will check my _____.

10

Well done! END OF SPELLING TEST 3!

10
MINS

Marks

1. Mum used a _____ to dig the garden.

2. I am _____ for a new bike for my birthday.

3. The stranger disappeared without a

_____.

4. When it's too hot I get a _____.

5. The children tidied _____ room.

6. We were _____ that our teacher was leaving.

7. In winter, our garden seems quite _____.

8. Dad helped me _____ a scarf for my teddy.

9. I am improving at _____.

10. My school uniform is good _____.

10

Well done! END OF SPELLING TEST 4!

Spelling Test 5

10 MINS

Marks

1. Beth began to _____ with the cold.

2. The thug _____ the policeman and ran off.

3. Dan likes _____ on one leg.

4. Mum and Dad are going on a _____ break.

5. There is a _____ in my shoelace.

6. Today, we have a _____ teacher.

7. Jamal _____ when he started the test.

8. I love going on long train _____.

9. There had been no _____ that it would rain so hard.

10. The teacher showed us how to _____ the ingredients.

10

Well done! END OF SPELLING TEST 5!

Marks

1. Bhavini _____ down her spellings.

2. The cows _____ across the field at feeding time.

3. Bella's new kitten is very _____.

4. Our neighbours have a _____ in their garden.

5. Mum _____ my bike.

6. Elephants are my favourite _____.

7. Tia wore a _____ hat for the parade.

8. Ollie saw a _____ spider in the garden.

9. The _____ for the school trip is due today.

10. I love orange and blackcurrant _____.

10

Well done! END OF SPELLING TEST 6!

Spelling Test 7

Marks

1. We began _____ the mushrooms.

2. I was hoping it wasn't the _____ answer.

3. Ahmed was _____ on the table.

4. Last night, there was a _____ storm.

5. We _____ the flour with the eggs.

6. There was a loud _____ on the door.

7. My puppy is very _____.

8. Freda loves _____ food.

9. Martha is the _____ girl in our class.

10. I made the _____ to read to the end of the book.

10

Well done! END OF SPELLING TEST 7!

Answers
Spelling

Q	Answers for Spelling the /j/ sound
1	pa**ge**, ri**dge**, sta**ge**, fu**dge**, bri**dge**, le**dge**, ra**ge**, nu**dge**, fri**dge**, smu**dge**, oran**ge**, hin**ge**
2	sle**dge**, he**dge**, ca**ge**, lar**ge**, ba**dger**
3	**j**acket, **j**am, **g**iraffes, **j**oin, ener**gy**

Q	Answers for Words ending le, el, al, il

	le	el
	tumble	tunnel
1	thimble	travel
	cable	towel

	al	il
	petal	pencil
1	pedal	nostril
	capital	pupil

Q	
2	squirr**el**, anim**al**, stenc**il**, comfortab**le**
3	shov**el**, hospit**al**, foss**il**, rumb**le**

Q	Answers for Suffixes 1
1	carried, carries; copied, copies; married, marries; cried, cries; worried, worries
2	heavier, funnier, lazier, nosier

	crazy	crazier	craziest
	lonely	lonelier	loneliest
	angry	**angrier**	**angriest**
3	**happy**	happier	**happiest**
	busy	**busier**	**busiest**
	noisy	noisier	**noisiest**

Q	
4	frying, carrying, trying, copying

Q	Answers for Suffixes 2
1	liked, liking; loved, loving; stared, staring; closed, closing
2	nicer, nicest; cuter, cutest; later, latest
3	baker, writer, dancer, gardener
4	bony, lazy, noisy, slimy

I	hummed, humming; dropped, dropping; ripped, ripping; clipped, clipping; tapped, tapping
2	runner, funny, winner, biggest
3	fattest, thinner, sunny, drummer, saggy
4	chopping, tripped, patting, chatter

5		ed	ing	er
	mix	**mixed**	mixing	mixer
	box	boxed	**boxing**	**boxer**

Q | **Answers for Suffixes 4**

I	enjoyment, agreement, payment, amazement, punishment
2	happiness, equipment, replacement, crispiness, dirtiness, measurement
3	hopeless, playful, quickly, silliness

4

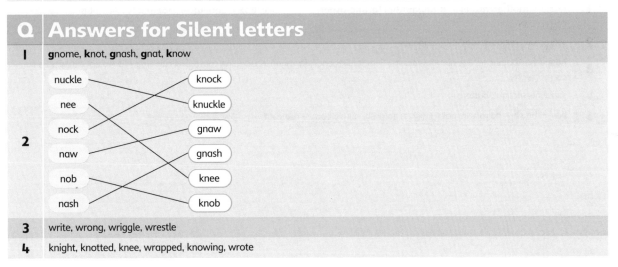

x	p	a	v	e	m	e	n	t
y	l	w	m	m	x	k	b	b
c	a	r	e	f	u	l	x	z
z	i	z	x	c	v	b	m	w
r	n	x	v	b	w	x	q	y
q	l	i	f	e	l	e	s	s
z	y	c	v	x	z	q	y	z

Q | **Answers for Silent letters**

I	**g**nome, **k**not, **g**nash, **g**nat, **k**now

2

nuckle	knock
nee	knuckle
nock	gnaw
naw	gnash
nob	knee
nash	knob

3	write, wrong, wriggle, wrestle
4	knight, knotted, knee, wrapped, knowing, wrote

1

c before **e**	c before **i**	c before **y**
pace	city	icy
trace	cinema	fancy
price	circle	cycle
dance	circus	spicy

2

¹m		²l		³f
e		a		o
⁴r	a	c	e	r
c		y		c
y				e

or

¹f		²l		³m
o		a		e
⁴r	a	c	e	r
c		y		c
e				y

3 space, dice, juicy, rice

1 subtraction, invention, celebration, correction, creation

2 indication, condition, injection, fiction, emotion

3 nation, mention, station, communication, position

1 bath + **room** = **bathroom**; web + **site** = **website**; play + **ground/time** =**playground/playtime**; grand + **mother/father** = **grandmother/grandfather**; shoe + **lace/box** = **shoelace/shoebox** NB Accept other possible correct words

2 scarecrow, rainbow, football, wallpaper

3 headache/toothache; upstairs/downstairs; fingernail/toenail; farmyard/backyard/courtyard; raindrop NB Accept other possible correct words

4 sunshine/sunlight, buttercup

5 hair + brush = hairbrush; gold + fish = goldfish; rain + coat = raincoat

Q Answers for Homophones

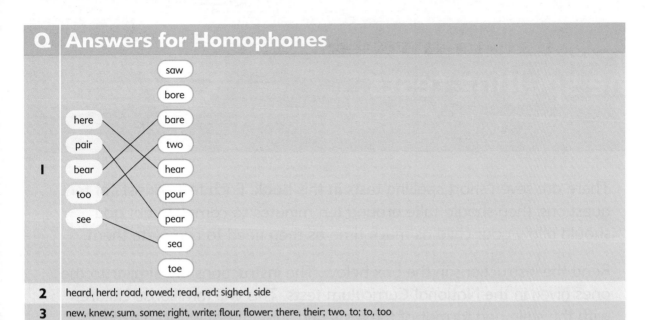

2 heard, herd; road, rowed; read, red; sighed, side

3 new, knew; sum, some; right, write; flour, flower; there, their; two, to; to, too

Q Answers for Tricky words

1 keys, donkeys, journeys

2 Answers will vary. Examples: monkeys, trolleys, chimneys

3 squash, quality, wasp, watch, wand

4 vision, division, treasure, pleasure, usual, measure, decision, leisure

How to administer the spelling tests

There are seven short spelling tests in this book. Each test consists of ten questions; they should take around ten minutes to complete but you should allow your child as much time as they need to complete them.

Read the instructions in the box below. The instructions are similar to the ones given in the National Curriculum tests. This will familiarise children with the style and format of the tests and show them what to expect.

> *Listen carefully to the instructions I am going to give you.*
>
> *I am going to read ten sentences to you. Each sentence on your answer sheet has a missing word. Listen carefully to the missing word and write it in the space provided, making sure you spell the word correctly. I will read the word, then the word within the sentence, then repeat the word a third time.*
>
> *Do you have any questions?*

Read the spellings as follows:

- Give the question number, 'Spelling 1'.
- Say, 'The word is...'.
- Read the whole sentence to show the word in context.
- Repeat, 'The word is...'.

Leave at least a 12-second gap between each spelling.

At the end, re-read all ten questions. Then say, 'This is the end of the test. Please put down your pencil or pen.'

Each correct answer should be awarded **1 mark**.